SPROUT
Branches Out

SPROUT

SPROUT
Branches Out

JESSIKA VON INNEREBNER

SCHOLASTIC INC.

*This story is dedicated
to all those messy moments
that encourage wonderful growth.
When you can grow where you are,
you can grow anywhere!*

ISBN 978-1-5461-2235-7

12 11 10 9 8 7 6 5 4 3 2 1   24 25 26 27 28 29

Printed in the U.S.A.   40

First Scholastic printing, January 2024

Book design by Ashley Caswell
This book was sprouted first on paper, then lovingly planted and tended to in Photoshop.

Somewhere in a little town, there is a small porch.

This is where Sprout lives.

She's only been able to grow two leaves, and Sprout is
ALWAYS ready to tell the other plants why.

Then one day,

BE
WILD
IN
NATURE
NOW!

SWEATER DOGS

something arrived . . .

. . . that moved Sprout into action.

She immediately packed up and took
off to find the perfect place to grow.

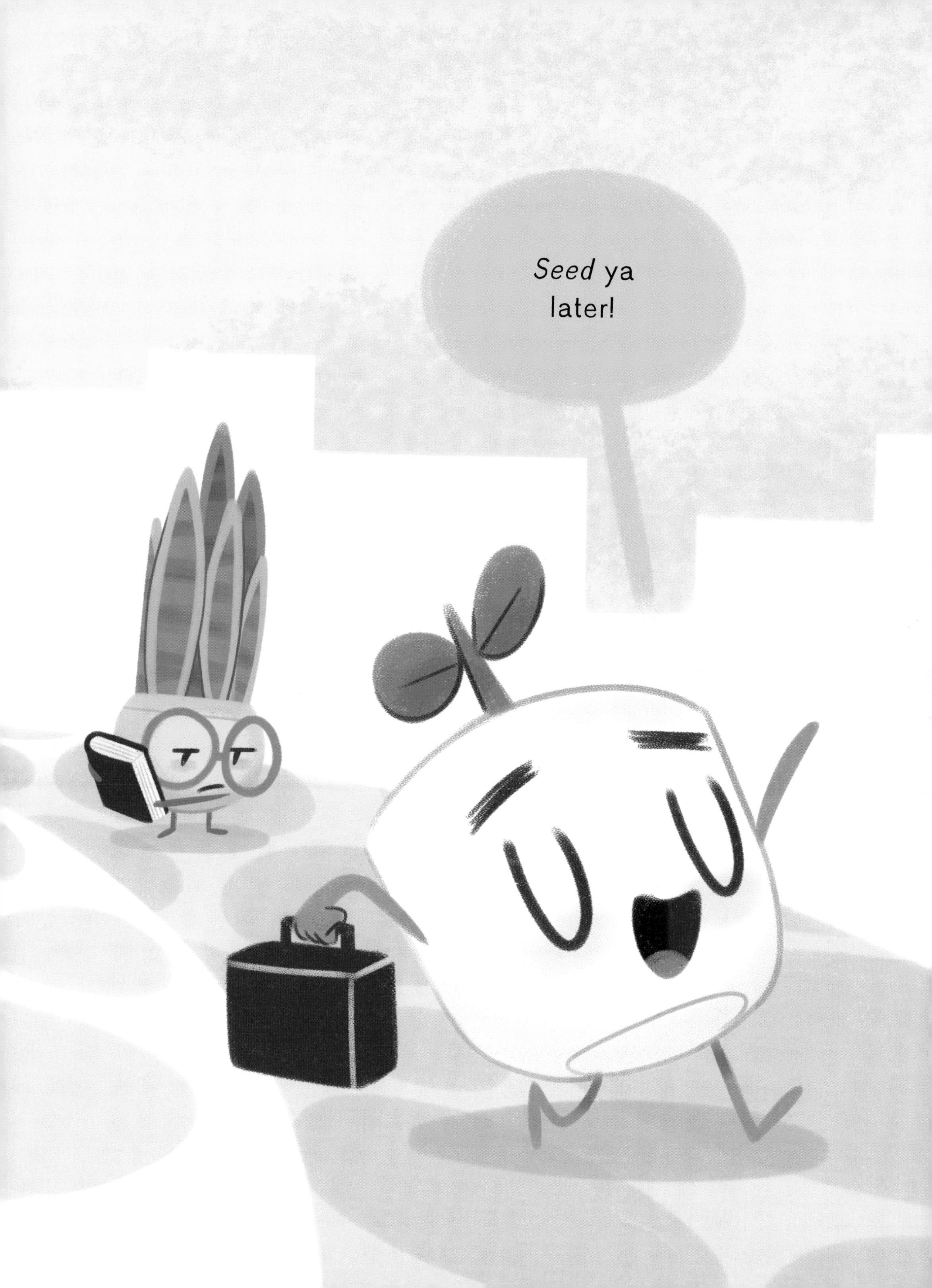
Seed ya later!

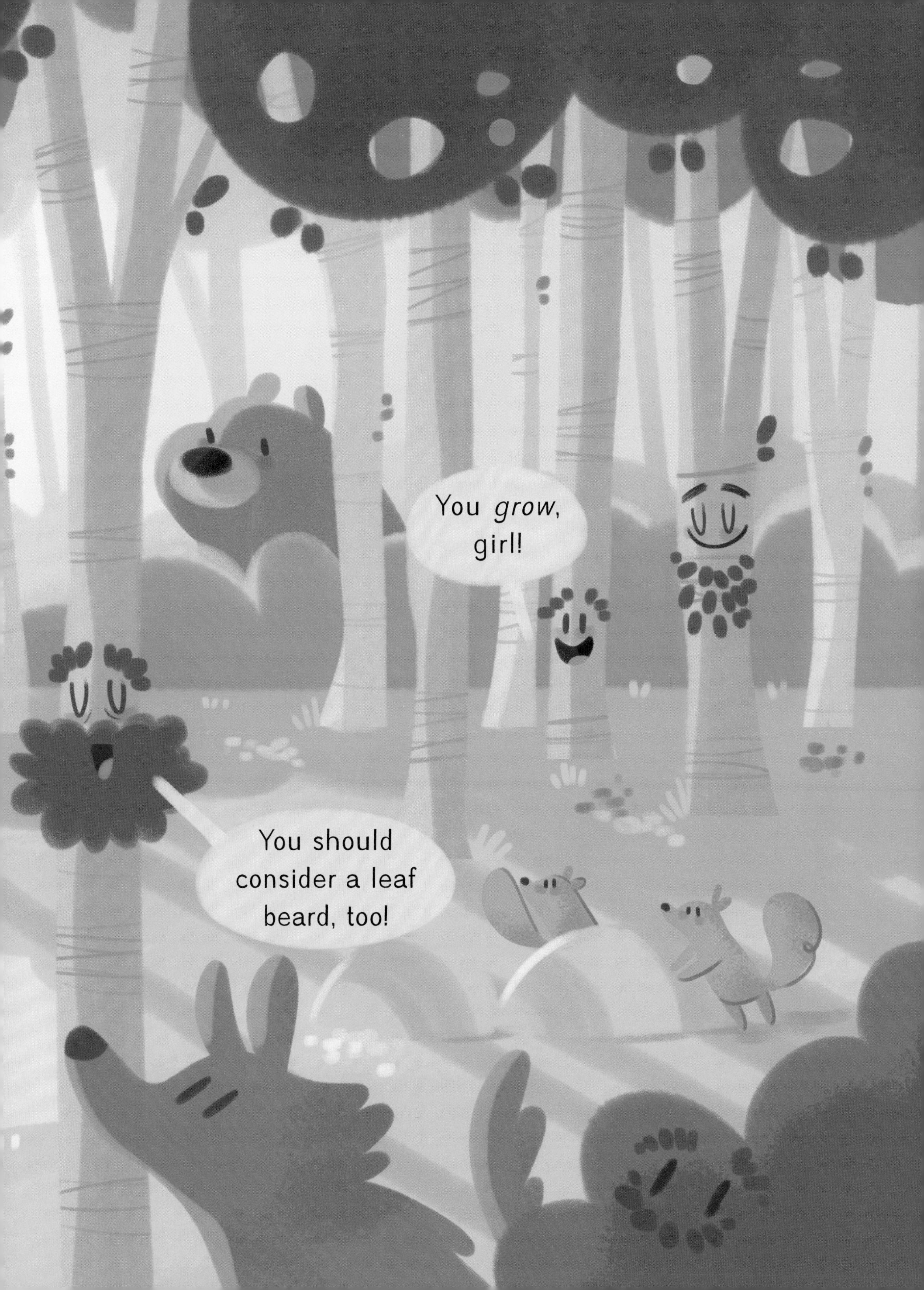
You *grow*, girl!
You should consider a leaf beard, too!

But that night,
Sprout realized it might be
a bit *too* wild for her. She wanted
the woods to put leaves on her chest,
not make her shake like one!

HOWL

SNARF

I think I wet
my *plants.*

GROWL

GRRRR...

With all that knowledge around her, Sprout knew she would grow bigger and faster than she could ever imagine.

This forest was way past elemen-*tree* for Sprout.
She wanted to grow fast, but not *that* fast.

But this was more rain than
Sprout had ever seen. She wanted
to drink water, not drown in it!

None of these places were
what she expected or needed.

Sprout felt lost and very confused.
She was supposed to be growing.
What was going on?

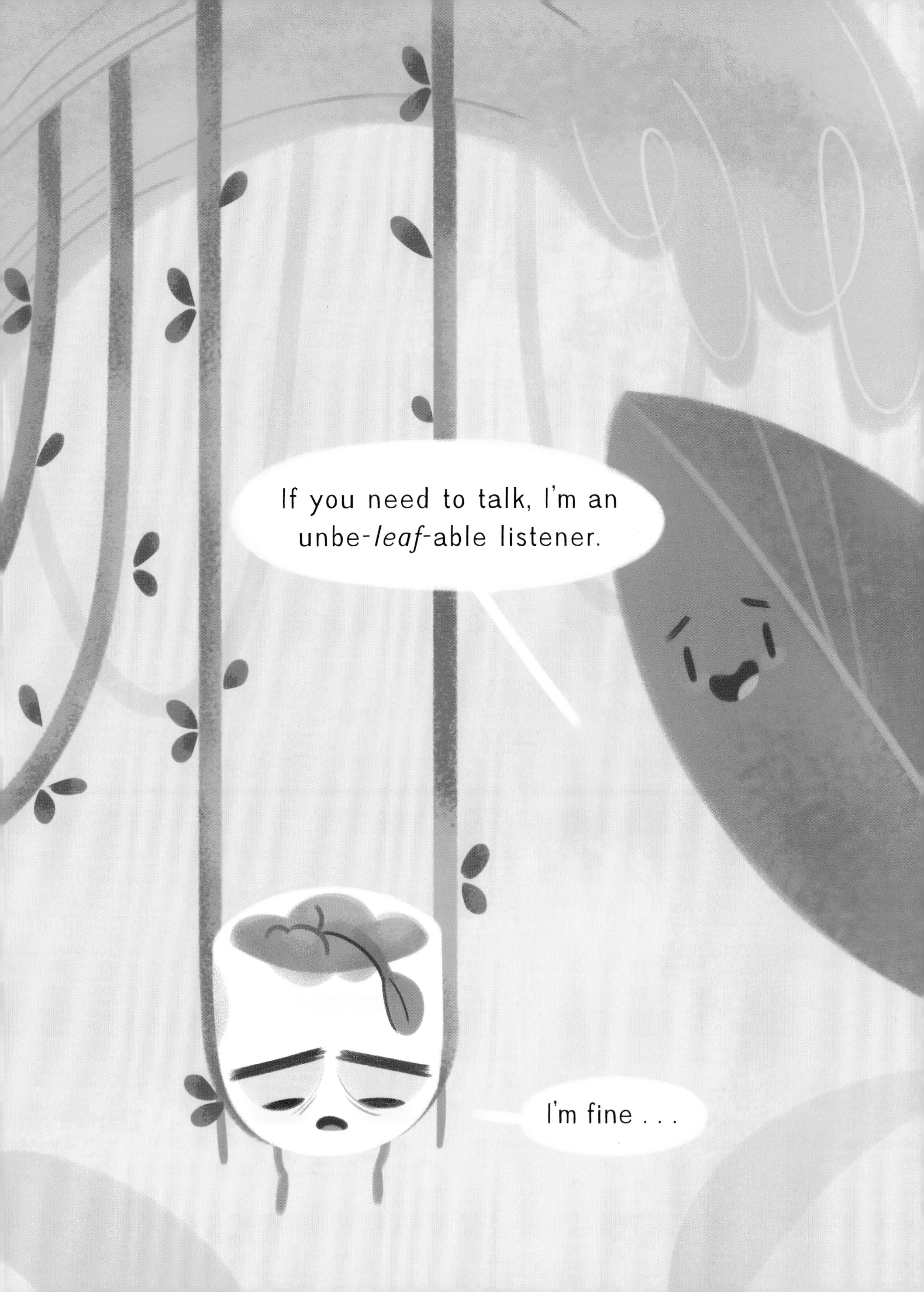
If you need to talk, I'm an unbe-*leaf*-able listener.
I'm fine . . .

Then it hit her.
Sprout knew exactly where she needed to be.

The small porch in the little town had everything Sprout had been looking for all along.

It had taken an adventure, but Sprout found her perfect place.

And you
know what . . .

She really started to grow.

SPROUT

GROW YOUR OWN SPROUT

Do you know how Sprout started out? All of those leaves and flowers she's growing began as a teeny-tiny seed. Lots of plants start from seeds, and there are many types of seeds, just like there are many types of plants! Sprout is a type of plant called a hydrangea, so she came from a hydrangea seed.

To grow your own plant,
ask a grown-up for some help gathering these materials:

A container and some soil—This is where your plant will grow. You can buy these in a store, or you can find them around your home and neighborhood.

Some seeds—Seeds come in all shapes and sizes. You can find them in nature, in a store, or even in your kitchen!

Water—Every plant is different, but all of them need water to grow healthy and strong, just like you!

After you plant your seed and give it some water, it's time to give your sprout a name and help it find sunlight. Some plants need lots of sun, and others need only a little.

Did you know that plants are great listeners?
Remember to talk to your plant and encourage it to grow.
Tell it about your day. Where did you go? What did you see?
Did you meet any friends, or learn anything new?
Your plant will love to hear all about it!

JESSIKA VON INNEREBNER is an author,
artist, imagination cultivator, adventurous
soul, and a creative thinker. If she were a
plant, she would be a monstera, because
even though she needs her space to
spread out, she also loves being around
others. Jessika has an awesome community
of *fronds* and has *grown* a lot because of
them. Though she often *leaves* in search
of excitement, Jessika always returns to
sunny Kelowna, Canada, where she lives with
her pup, Charlie, and hubby, Cale.